Jakki Wood studied graphic design at Wolverhampton Polytechnic.
She has written and illustrated many children's books for Frances Lincoln,
including *Animal Parade*, *Baby Parade*, *Number Parade*, *Fiddle-I-fee*,
Noisy Parade, *Bumper to Bumper* and *March of the Dinosaurs*.
Jakki lives in Worcestershire.

To Jack Michael

First published in Great Britain in 1998 by
Frances Lincoln Children's Books, 4 Torriano Mews
Torriano Avenue, London NW5 2RZ
www.franceslincoln.com

This paperback edition published in 2006

The author and publishers would like to thank Stephen Hall
of the Southampton Oceanography Centre for this help.

British Library Cataloguing in Publication Data available on request

ISBN-10: 1-84507-538-2
ISBN-13: 978-1-84507-538-5

Printed in China

1 3 5 7 9 8 6 4 2

THE DEEP BLUE SEA

An Ocean Wildlife Book

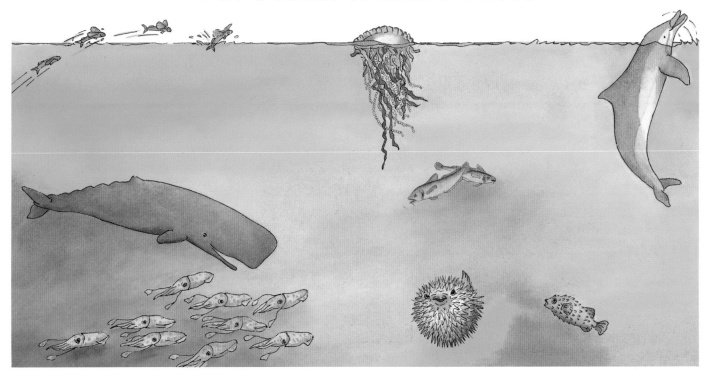

Jakki Wood

FRANCES LINCOLN CHILDREN'S BOOKS

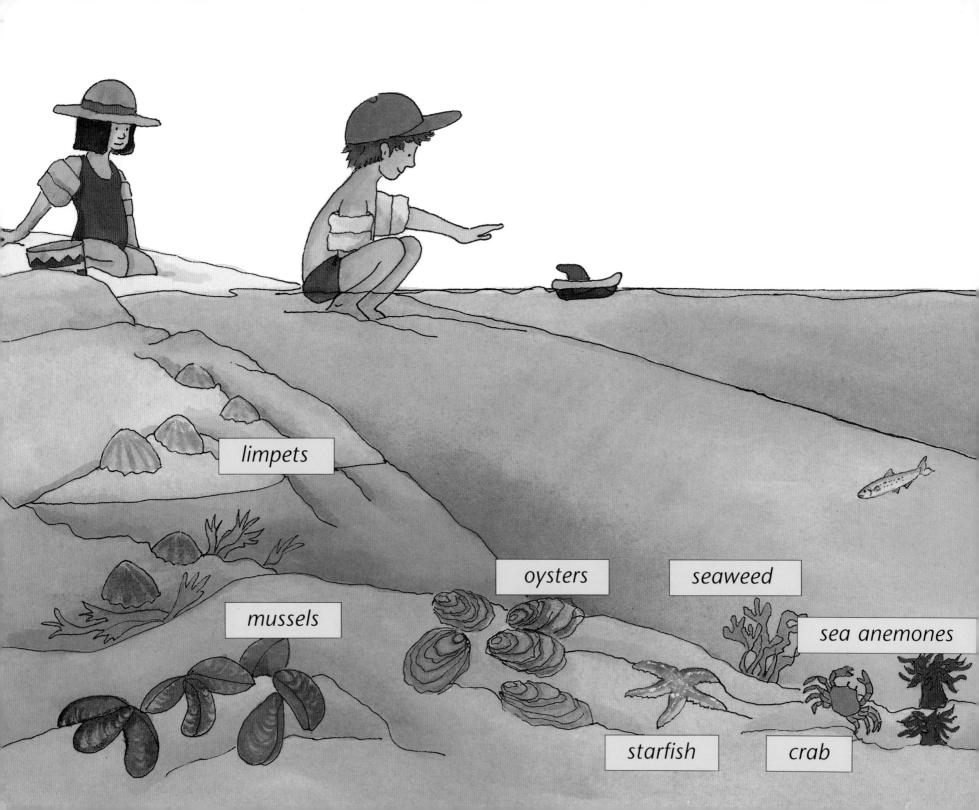

limpets

mussels

oysters

seaweed

sea anemones

starfish

crab

On the beach in California, Tom gives his boat a *push!*

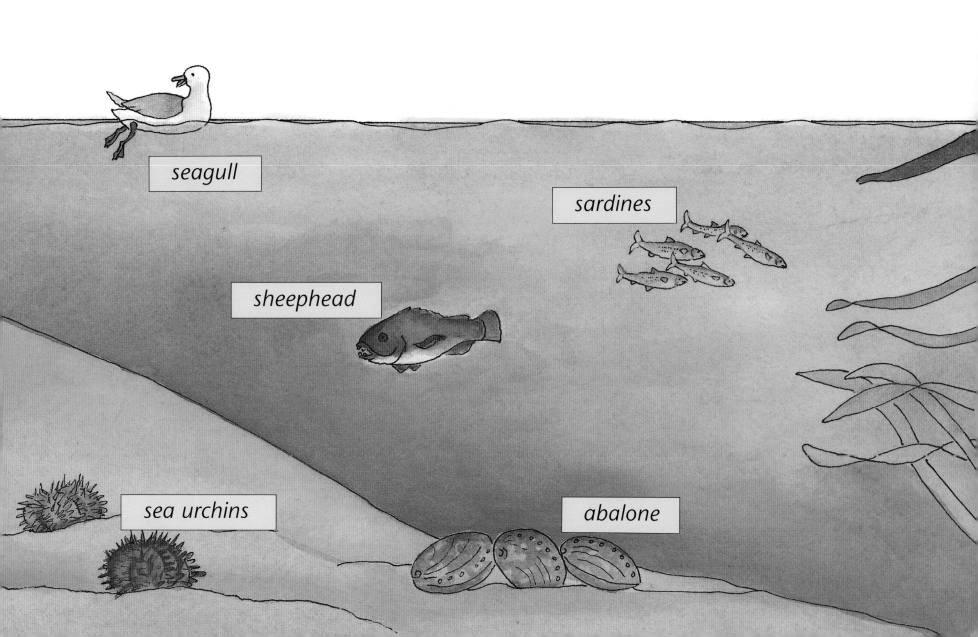

It drifts away on the ocean currents.

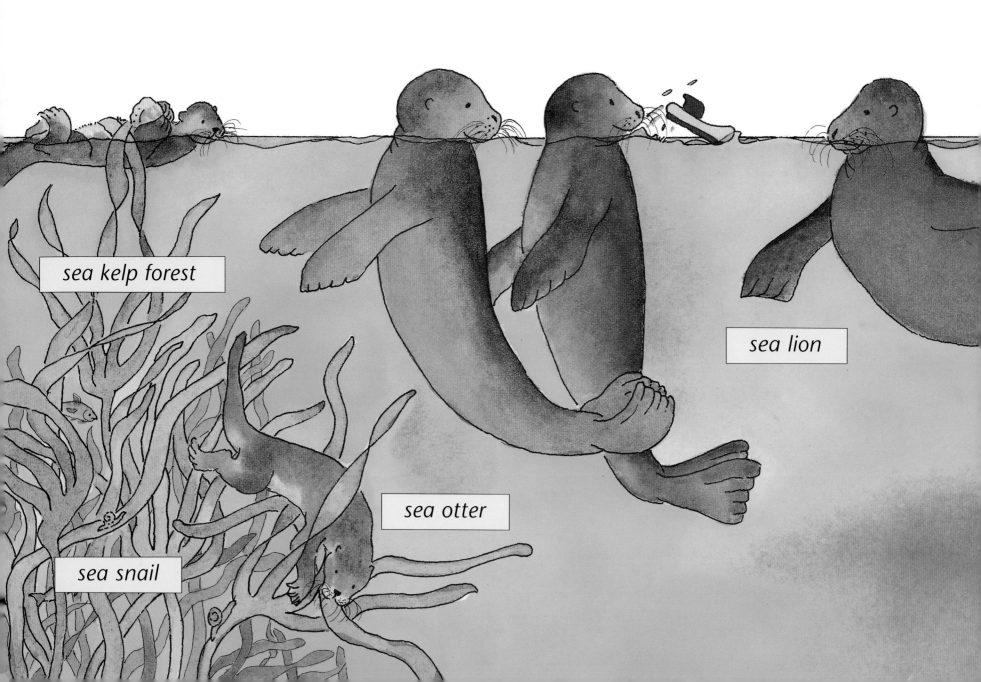

sea kelp forest

sea lion

sea otter

sea snail

brown pelican

anchovies

Out in the Pacific, killer whales play with Tom's boat ...

tuna

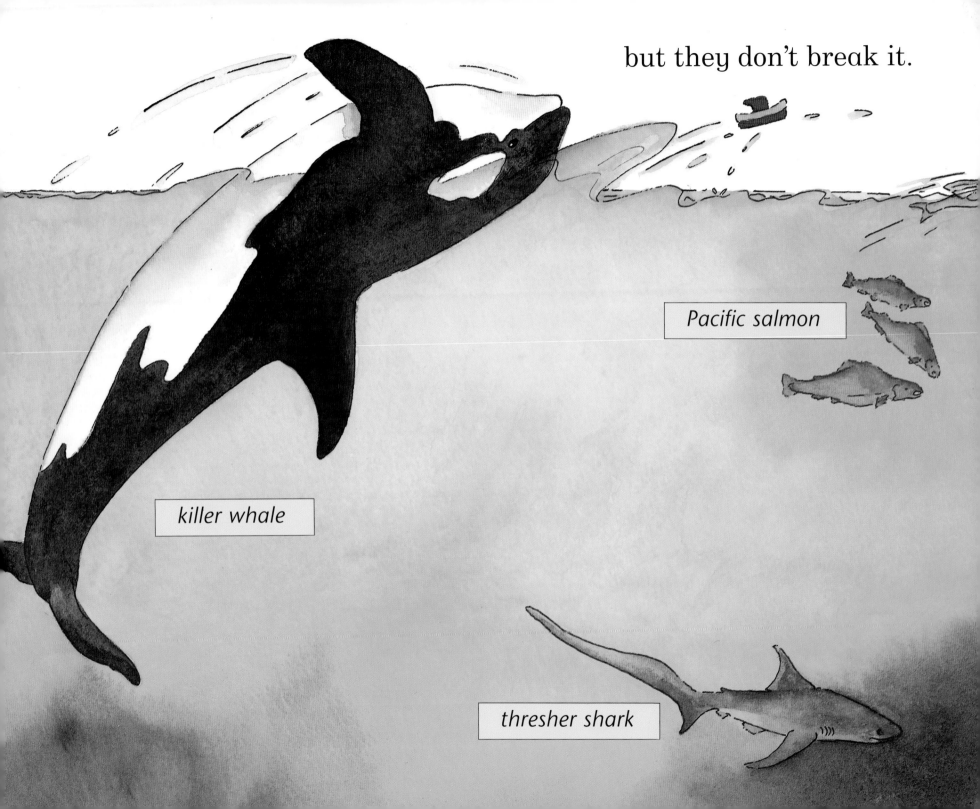

but they don't break it.

Pacific salmon

killer whale

thresher shark

Splash! Flying fish leap and glide.

flying fish

grey whale

octopus

black smoker

Tom's boat is just north of Australia,
near a tiny coral island.

manta ray

hammerhead sharks

sponge

lobster

sea cucumber

brittle star

swordfish

parrot fish

coral reef

grouper

lion fish

giant clam

butterfly fish

sea anemone

A friendly turtle gives the boat a ride.

clownfish

trunkfish

loggerhead turtle

In the Indian Ocean, a great storm blows up.

scad

Fish swim calmly beneath the waves.

whalebird

macaroni penguin

Safe from the storm, south of Africa,
the boat is noticed by some curious penguins ...

krill

Southern fur seal

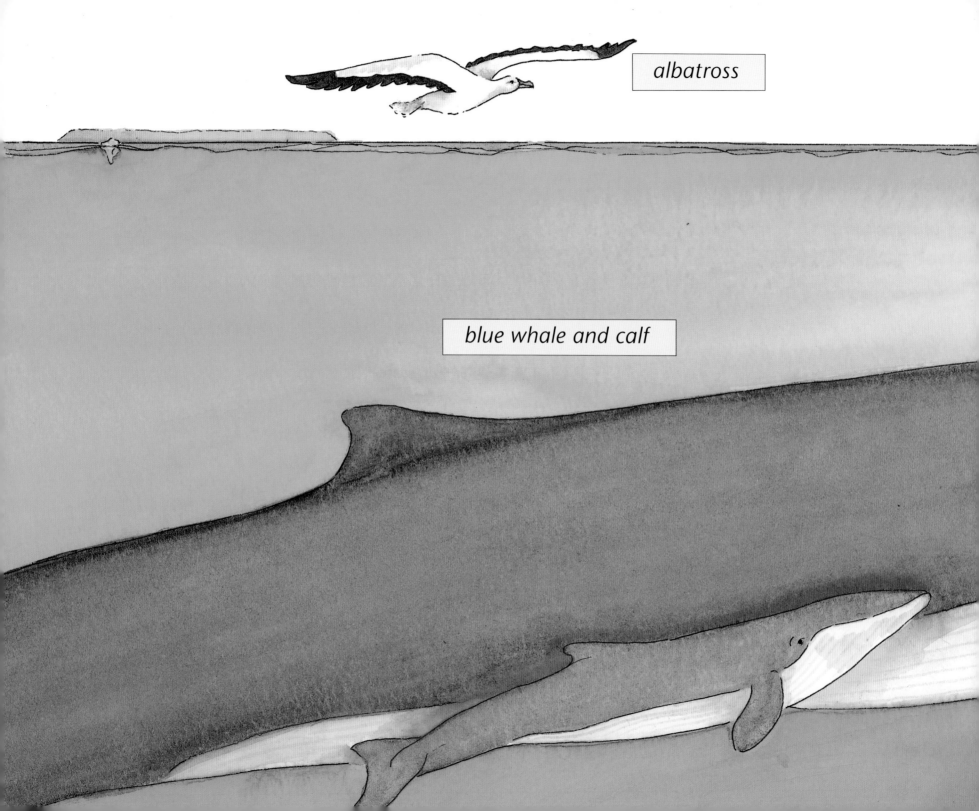

albatross

blue whale and calf

and watched by a huge blue whale.

Tom's boat has reached the Atlantic Ocean.

flying fish

Portuguese man-of-war

sperm whale

hake

puffer fish

squid

The dolphins would like to keep it.

common dolphin

But the warm current carries it above the wreck of a pirate ship ...

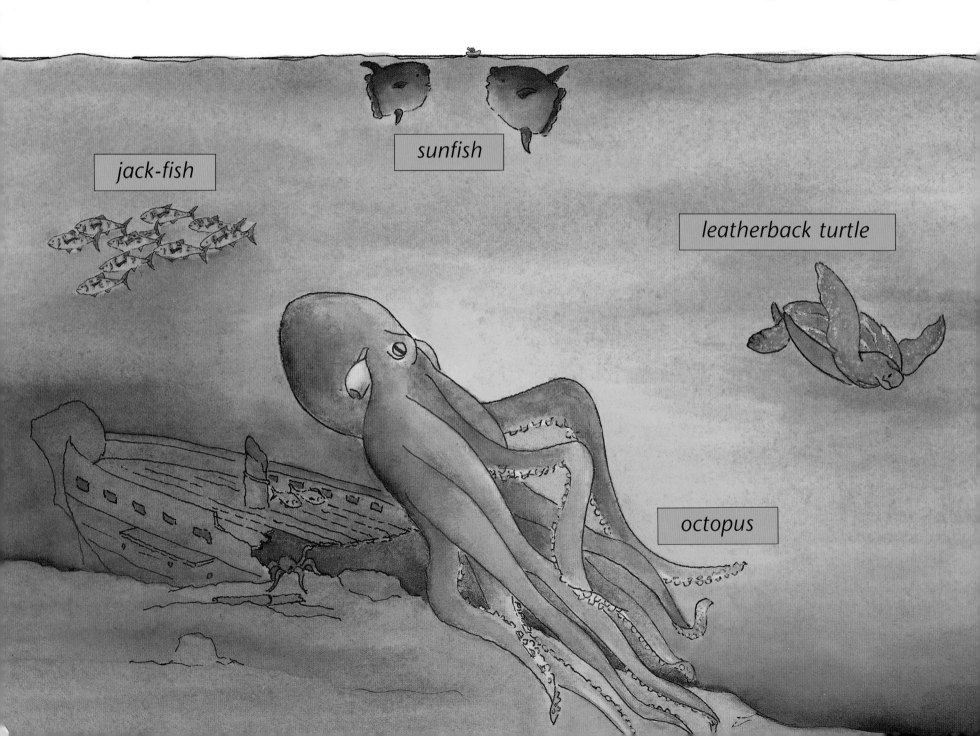

sunfish

jack-fish

leatherback turtle

octopus

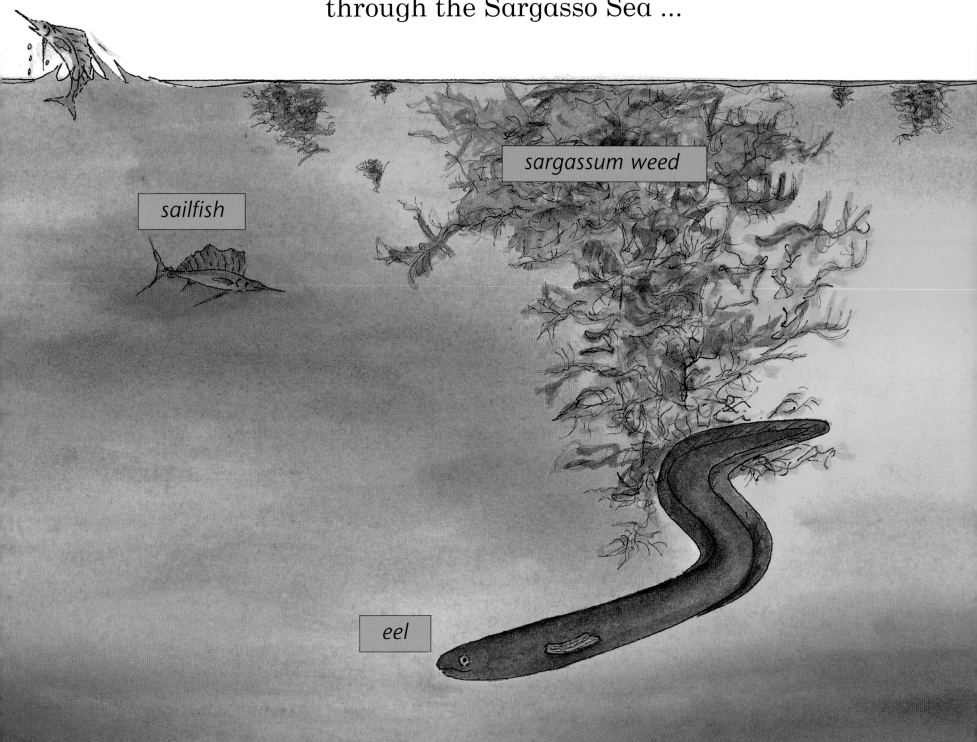

sailfish

sargassum weed

eel

and right across the Atlantic Ocean.

porbeagle shark

hatchet fish

angler fish

gulper eel

Far, far below, strange creatures swim in the dark water.

squid

black smoker

At last Tom's boat is close to land again.

cormorant

herring

A dolphin pushes it towards the shore.

bottlenose dolphin

pilot whale

A boy reaches into the water,
and grabs the red-and-yellow boat.

seagull

puffin

stingray

cod

grey seal

John Dory

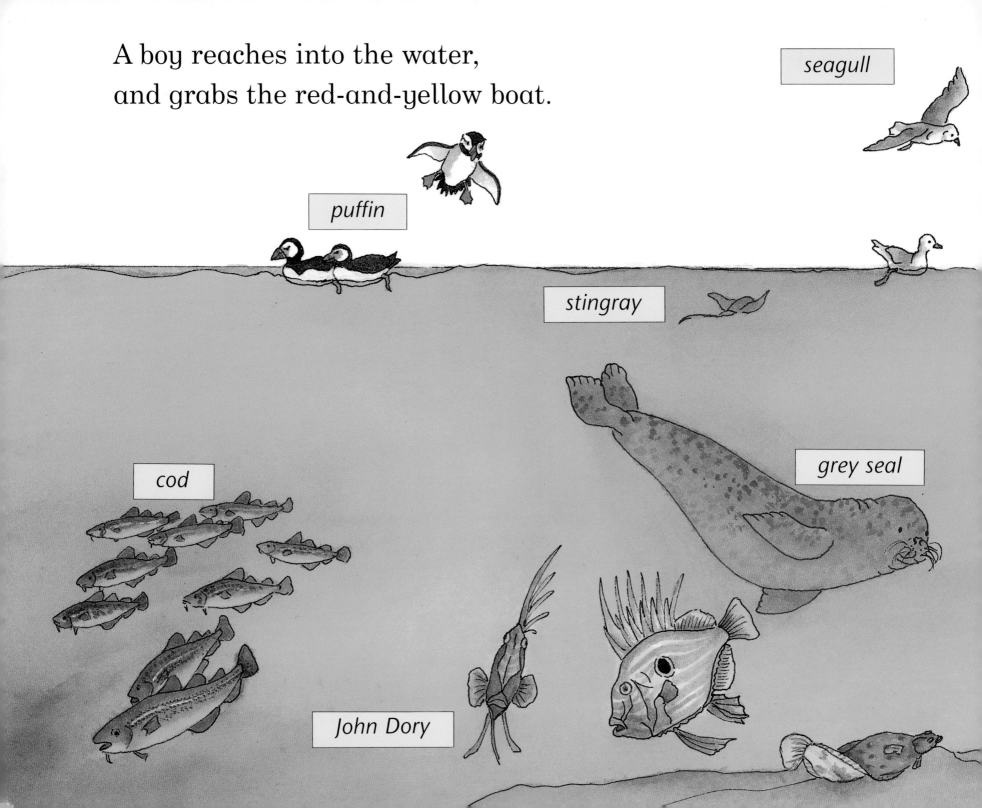

Tom's boat has drifted all the way to Britain.
Now someone else will play with it.

mackerel

crab

plaice

cockles

Can you follow the little boat's journey? The blue line shows the route it takes, drifting with the wind and the ocean currents.

Look at some of the fish and other sea creatures on the map. They will help you to match areas of the map to the story inside. Follow the arrows from California on the western coast of the USA, to Cornwall in southwest England – a sea journey of more than 40,000 kilometres.

puffin

Europe

bottlenose dolphin

angler fish

eel

sargassum weed

octopus

CARIBBEAN SEA

Africa

Portuguese man-of-war

blue whale

ATLANTIC OCEAN

macaroni penguin

SOUTHERN OCEAN

North America

Asia

sardines

sea otter

INDIAN
OCEAN

loggerhead
turtle

hammerhead
shark

flying
fish

killer
whale

PACIFIC
OCEAN

South America

scad

Australia